Introduction

Caves are part of a world that most of us rarely see. Yet, below the surface of the land there are powerful raging rivers, caverns as big as the largest football stadiums, and tunnels wider than a motorway. Inside the caves are strange sculptures and wonderful rock formations, scenery as fantastic and beautiful as anything upon the land surface.

Caves instil wonder and excitement in all who enter them, be they casual visitors wandering through a show cave or true sporting enthusiasts who seek to explore their secrets. Caves are dark and mysterious, and few have been completely explored even today. We still have much to learn about the subterranean world: its geology, hydrology, biology and archaeology.

Porth yr Ogof is one of the most impressive and best known caves in Britain. It has the largest cave entrance in Wales, and one of the largest in the British Isles. It is in every respect a special place; the setting, the atmosphere, the

A busy day at Porth yr Ogof car park.

insight it provides to the wonders of the natural world beneath our feet, renders it an ideal venue for introductory caving activity. Today, well over 30,000 people a year visit Porth yr Ogof to savour the unique underground experience.

The cave lies near the small village of Ystradfellte (grid ref. SN 930135), at the southern boundary of the Brecon Beacons National Park. Despite its setting – less than five miles from the urban centres at the head of the valleys dissecting the South Wales coalfield – this is truly an area of outstanding natural beauty. The approach roads are narrow and twisting, the landscape dominated by wild, windswept mountains to the north, and a deep wooded valley to the south, separated by a patchwork of small fields and an occasional farmstead.

On reaching the bottom of the wooded Mellte valley there is, at first sight, little indication of anything unusual. The more observant visitor, however, will quickly realise that the river – afon Mellte – is nowhere to be seen. The road crosses a dry valley floor. Furthermore, the river channel down-valley of the road is also dry for a distance of about 200 metres, although here and there the sound of rushing water can be heard at the bottom of dark and mysterious caves. But up-valley of the lowest point, the ground falls away very steeply and it is in the gorge, completely invisible from the road above, that the impressive Main Entrance to Porth yr Ogof is situated. The road, therefore, bridges the cave through which flows afon Mellte. Above the lip of the gorge is a spacious car park supervised seven days a week by an employee of the National Park.

Porth yr Ogof looking up river

Many people – young and old – are surprised to learn that most of the land in a National Park is privately owned. At Porth yr Ogof, however, the Brecon Beacons National Park Authority were fortunate to be able to acquire an area of land on a 999 year lease, granted by the Secretary of State for Wales in 1991, thereby ensuring public access for all time. The acquisition also ensures that any

A group of young cavers being briefed at the notice board in the car park.

development in the vicinity can be controlled, and that the area can be effectively monitored and carefully managed so as to conserve the environment for future generations.

The geological background

Porth yr Ogof lies on the afon Mellte, a tributary of the River Neath, some 250 metres above sea level. In the vicinity of Ystradfellte a relatively narrow belt of limestone – **Carboniferous Limestone** – sandwiched between the Old Red Sandstone to the north and the Millstone Grit to the south. Unlike the neighbouring rocks to the north and south, Carboniferous Limestone has one unique quality – it is capable of being dissolved by mildly acidic water. The rock is also permeable, which means that water seeps and flows through the limestone along an intricate network of natural cracks and fissures. The vertical cracks are known as **joints**, while the horizontal divisions are known as **bedding planes**.

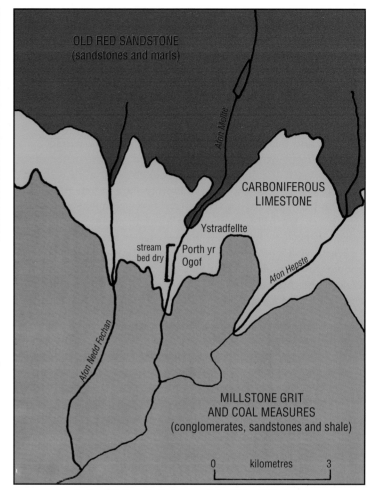

A simplified geological map of the Ystradfellte area

Standing at the impressive Main Entrance to the cave it is possible to pick out both of these sets of cracks and begin to gain an understanding of how caves form. Due to its uptake of carbon dioxide from the atmosphere, rainwater contains a very weak acid – **carbonic acid** – and it is this which acts chemically upon the limestone to dissolve it away. The water seeps slowly into the cracks and over a period of many tens of thousands of years enlarges them to form the passages and caves which we see today. Once the passage reaches a certain size, the chemical process whereby the rock is dissolved away is helped by a secondary mechanical action: sand, pebbles and boulders, carried by the river when in flood, will further grind away the floor and walls of a cave, an action best compared to the action of a file on metal or sandpaper on wood.

Rainfall in this area amounts to approximately 2,300 mm (90 inches) a year, double that at the coast about 18 miles to the south. Further north in the Brecon Beacons totals are much higher. The rainfall gathers in a network of tiny streams which merge to flow south as afon Mellte. The river flows in a normal fashion until it crosses the geological boundary and meets the limestone, a short distance down-valley of Ystradfellte. Here, at a place known as Church Sink, the water quietly disappears into a set of cracks and rubble-filled fissures on the south bank.

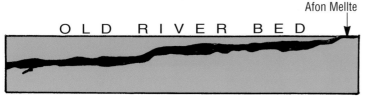

Course of Mellte prior to cavern collapse.

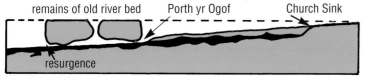

Course of the Mellte today.

Church Sink near Ystradfellte village: this is the point where, under normal water conditions, the river disappears underground, not to be seen again until the Tradesman's Entrance at Porth yr Ogof.

Afon Mellte in flood; on rare occasions the river will fill the Main Entrance to the roof.

Down-valley of Church Sink the stream course is normally dry during the summer months all the way to Porth yr Ogof, a distance of about one kilometre. However, as the absence of any grass or vegetation in the stream bed suggests, the river responds rapidly to rainfall. In wet weather the small pool of water at Church Sink soon fills up to overflowing and afon Mellte continues along the surface just like any other river. Geographers call such a river an intermittent stream.

At Porth yr Ogof the river disappears underground, no matter how heavy or prolonged the rainfall may have been. Afon Mellte (meaning the 'lightening river') can rise with alarming speed and when in flood the Main Entrance makes an impressive spectacle. At such times the ledges which lead towards the cave become submerged, and in exceptional floods, which occur, perhaps, twice a year, water may rise to the very roof of the Main Entrance. Leaves, twigs and other debris lodged in small cracks in the cave roof are evidence of past floods, as too are the huge tree trunks which lie wedged here and there between the passage walls. It is extremely important that all cavers develop an awareness of these tell-tale signs of flood danger.

Moving into the cave proper aids geological understanding for the fossils visible in the thick layers of limestone exposed on the floor, in the side walls and in the roof of the cave indicate that the rock was laid down on the floor of a warm tropical sea, in an environment similar to the Bahamas, or the Caribbean, today. Over the course of geological time the original soft layers of sediment containing the remains of shells, crinoids (sea lilies) and corals compacted to form rock. The fossilised remains of large cockle-like and snail-like shells are particularly common and their presence remind the visitor of the clear, tropical seas in which they lived and died about 340 million years ago.

Later still, in one of the great periods of mountain building the rocks were lifted from the ocean bed and tilted so that today the layers of strata in this area dip gently to the south at an angle of about 5 degrees. However, this simple arrangement has been complicated by the development of cracks or **faults**, which can be studied far better underground than on the surface. Above ground, rocks are covered by soil and vegetation but in the cave every detail can be seen, together with the influence of joints, bedding planes and faults on cave direction and roof stability.

Some Carboniferous Limestone fossils

A sea shell (brachiopod)

Round, cross sections of crinoid stems
(1p coin for scale)

A prominent fossil sea snail (gastropod) on the floor of the passage between the Letter Box squeeze and the Creek
(£1.00 coin for scale)

Geological diagram showing the sedimentary rock structure in the area

Deposition of strata on the floor of shallow seas and coastal lowlands.

Coal Measures
Millstone Grit
Carboniferous Limestone
Old Red Sandstone

Uplift, due to major earth movements, and tilting of rock layers towards the south.

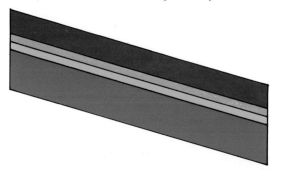

Erosion by the action of weather, rivers and ice, to produce the present landscape.

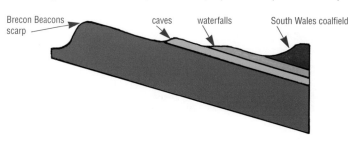

Brecon Beacons scarp

caves

waterfalls

South Wales coalfield

Cave formation

Given access to the heart of Carboniferous Limestone, water begins its dual function of destruction and construction. In the first instance, the chemical processes at work simply dissolves the rock. In time, the trickle of water in larger fissures will capture the water seeping along smaller cracks in the surrounding rock. As a result of this increased flow, the rock dissolves more quickly, and slowly – ever so slowly – a seeping, waterlogged fissure will be enlarged to form a cave.

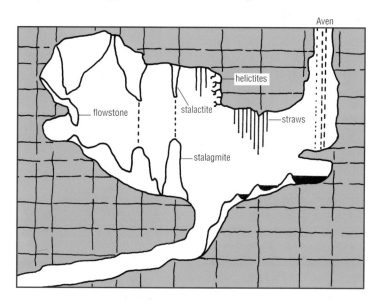

Aven

helictites

flowstone

stalactite

straws

stalagmite

In the earliest stage of cave development the underground passage will be completely flooded. This is known as the **phreatic stage** of development.

Stages in the development of a phreatic tube on a bedding plane

Later, as water-levels drop – which may happen, for example, as rivers carve ever deeper into their valley floors, or glaciers gouge and deepen their channels – some of the higher tunnels (the first to be formed) will be occupied by free-flowing streams capable of eroding channels in the cave floor. Much later, these 'old' waterways may be completely abandoned and such dry tunnels are sometimes referred to as 'fossil passages'.

Passages which were once full of water have a distinctive round or elliptical cross-section. A very good example can be seen in the west wall, directly beneath the roof, at the Main Entrance. Here a beautiful, small, phreatic tube-way, less than a metre in diameter, and developed upon a very prominent bedding plane, winds off into the darkness. Another example lies at roof level in the east wall, directly upstream of the White Horse Pool.

In the later **vadose stage** of cave development, when a stream runs freely along the cave floor, below an airspace, the cave frequently develops a trench-like form produced by down-cutting. Very simply, first-stage passages are characterised by wonderful tubular shapes, while second-stage developments are typically tall, narrow fissures or canyons. Some passages will possess a combination of both features, and their shape is often compared to a 'key-hole' when viewed in cross section. Limited examples of vadose development can be seen in the area known as the Creek.

Other features which are associated with the erosion and sculpting of caves are **shafts** or **potholes**, where water has, at some stage, found an easy vertical route through the rock layers. Large **chambers** or **caverns** may develop, for example, where two major fissures intersect, and their floors are frequently littered with boulders which have fallen from the roof above. There are two excellent examples of potholes close to and above the Letter Box squeeze; cavers are often seen climbing, or abseiling in one or other of these shafts.

The phreatic tube developed on a bedding plane situated in the west wall of the Main Entrance

The Creek is a particularly well sculpted passage with fine phreatic tubeways developed upon bedding planes.

When out walking in limestone areas anywhere in the British Isles **it is extremely important never to drop stones, or anything else, into potholes:** in the past, cavers at the bottom of shafts have been killed by the thoughtless actions of passers-by!

Cave decorations

While nature on the one hand seeks to carve out and modify passageways through the limestone, so too does she seek to decorate this secret world of darkness. Here and there, rare cave formations of exquisite beauty are encountered. These decorations are, like the caves themselves, a product of flowing water. As water seeps slowly through minute fissures in the rock it carries with it the limestone it has dissolved along the way. However, the water eventually finds its way into an air-space within a cave passage and there it will release some of the carbon dioxide gas held in solution. This, in turn, results in some of the dissolved rock being precipitated in the form of a white crystalline mineral known as **calcite**.

A small droplet of water emerging on the roof of a cave passage will deposit a microscopic ring of calcite before it falls to the floor. Day after day, year after year, over hundreds or even thousands of years, this process continues, resulting in the growth of a pure white, delicate, **stalactite** straw. Like an ever lengthening drinking straw or a constantly growing packet of Polo mints, the crystalline structure extends downward to form a 'frozen-looking' stalactite. Some-times the hollow space at the centre of the straw will block, forcing the water to seep out just above the constriction. Many years later the stalactite will appear like some pendulous, carrot-shaped formation.

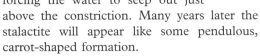

Stages in the development of a stalactite straw

When the water droplet falls to the cave floor, yet more calcite is deposited – provided, of course, there is no stream present to wash it away. In this case the product is a stumpy, crystalline mass which grows slowly upward to form a **stalagmite**.

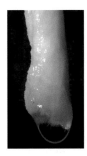

The Great Bedding Cave, looking downstream

When a stalactite and stalagmite meet, the outcome is a **pillar** or **column**, such as the array of formations which can be viewed from the rocky banks of the river in the Great Bedding Cave or, better still, in Hywel's Grotto.

Changes above ground, such as a rapid climatic cooling leading to the onset of an ice age, will have an effect upon the underworld. When the surface of the land is blanketed in snow and ice, as was the case during the last Ice Age, 20,000 years ago, less water will enter the cave system and consequently erosion is reduced. Later, as the ice melts, dramatic floods may wash mud, sand and stones into the caves sometimes completely blocking the point at which water originally found its way underground. In Porth yr Ogof this has happened at Mud Hall between White Horse Pool and the Tradesman's Entrance.

> Remember, stalac**tites** cling on **tight** to the ceiling; stalag**mites might** grow up!

A 30 metre crawl must be negotiated to reach a fine set of calcite formations in Hywel's Grotto.

At a later date, a stream may re-excavate an old water course or even find a new route. This has happened in the vicinity of Mud Hall and an experienced leader would draw to the attention of his party the underside of the calcite shelf which protrudes from the left wall, 50 metres downstream of the Tradesman's Entrance. Here, the upper layers of rounded cobbles, which were washed into the cave many, many thousands of years ago, were later cemented together by a coating of calcite. In comparatively recent geological time, the cave stream has carved its way down through the cobble bank and washed the lower, uncemented mud and cobbles away. Today, therefore, this short section of passage is left with an overhanging ledge of flowstone beneath which flows the stream.

The fascinating thing is that Porth yr Ogof reflects all these changes or stages in its history to those who care to stop and look. Caves are, in a very real sense, 'time capsules' and can tell us much about the recent geological history of our planet.

> A crystal structure which may have taken thousands of years to form can be easily destroyed, leading to the loss of a priceless wonder for all time. One small touch is often all it takes to destroy a stalactite. It is very important, therefore, that they, like all cave formations, remain as first discovered, for others to enjoy.

Porth yr Ogof in history

Porth yr Ogof has been known for many hundreds of years. However, unlike the caves of the Gower peninsula, or the Bone Cave (Ogof yr Esgyrn) at the Dan yr Ogof show cave complex in the upper Swansea valley, no evidence of prehistoric human occupation of this site has been found to date. This is hardly surprising given the fact that most of the passageways are susceptible to severe flooding after prolonged or heavy rainfall. Porth yr Ogof would not have been an inviting shelter to the early inhabitants of the area.

In more recent times the cave has been described by many visiting travellers and their vivid and often romantic descriptions would certainly have encouraged others to explore the natural wonders of the area. In 1698 the famous naturalist Edward Llwyd commented on the fossil shells to be seen within Porth yr Ogof:

> On the sides as well as the bottom of a noted cave called Porth Gogo at Ystrad Velhte in Brecknockshire I have observed several remains of Cockles half worn by the swift Current of the River Melte which runs through the cave and polishes its limestone.

A fuller description of the cave itself is to be found in Theophilus Jones' county chronicle, *The History of the County of Brecknock* (1805):

> In the summer season, when the river is low, it runs in a confined rocky channel until it flows opposite the village of Ystradfellte, when it steals into a small whirlpool on the south bank, where it is lost: the channel however which it pursues in the time of floods is seen covered with stones for about half a mile until we come to a cave below, called Porth yr Ogof, or the mouth of the cave; here the banks on both sides are nearly precipitous . . . creeping on all fours on the left, on entering, we discover a nearly perfect concave dome, from the roof of which are suspended stalactites and other calcareous concretions in great abundance, which make a brilliant appearance when lights are introduced. On the same side of the river, a little lower and further into the cave, the river Mellte is heard, rippling over the stones and soon afterwards it falls into a tremendous deep and black pool in the centre of the cavern. The different sounds of the water babbling above as it approaches, from that which is heard upon its fall into this whirlpool are striking, and the whole of the scene horridly grand: at the lower end of this gulf in a black rock, is a vein of calcareous spar [calcite], which is supposed to resemble a naked child standing upon a pedestal,

from whence it is called Llyn y baban (the pool of the baby), here the river is again lost, for about one or two hundred yards [180m], after which, in floods, it boils out below with great fury.

On the right or northern side of the cave again is another branch of the cavern, which is said to extend many miles in length, where persons have lost their way and never returned . . .

A short distance down-valley of Porth yr Ogof are the Clun Gwyn falls, a series of spectacular waterfalls where the river cascades in sheets of pure sparkling silver over rock steps. Jones' description of the area is most vivid:

> . . . the rage of this mountain torrent (after leaving the cave) is such during a flood as completely to divest it during its descent of the appearance of water; all is vapour, foam and wild confusion. At one time it falls in an unbroken cascade, and produces a misty cloud for several yards round, it then rolls and tumbles in such fantastic directions, and we could almost say shapes, being buffeted from side to side by the irregular obstructions of projecting rocks on its banks for upwards of three miles, as cannot be described, until it loses its name in the Neath, and with it in a great measure its wrath.

Benjamin Heath Malkin visited the cave in 1803, two years before the publication of Jones' book. Like Jones he could not resist publishing in his volume, *The Scenery, Antiquities, and Biography of South Wales* (1804), an account of the cave between the Main Entrance and the Resurgence:

> There is a practicable passage through it; but the attempt is imprudent. It is necessary to carry candles; and if they are extinguished by the damp vapour, the difficulty and danger become very great. In one instance, a life was lost; though my guide had been through several times, and was ready to undertake it with any visitor. We penetrated about a 100 yards [90 m], as far as any glimmering of daylight from the mouth directed us: and this specimen of Stygian horror was amply sufficient to satisfy all rational curiosity.

Porth yr Ogof
The engraving by Watson & Radclyffe is dated 1837.

Sgwd yr Eira on Afon Hepste
A nineteenth-century engraving published by Cassell & Co. Ltd.

The White Horse Pool is several metres in depth and great caution must be exercised in such areas.

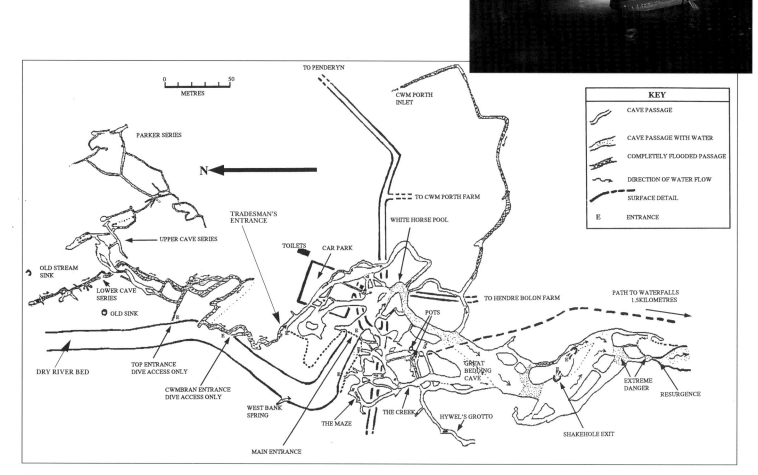

Legend and folklore

Theophilus Jones was of the opinion that the forces of nature, combined with the isolation of the valley, had an influence upon the character and beliefs of local inhabitants:

> We are almost inclined to think that the wilderness of character and peculiarity of feature of the scenery of this country have in some degree affected the opinions of the inhabitants, and have contributed to preserve among them a greater number of the legends of antiquity, and a stronger faith in old tales about ghosts and hobgoblins than in any other part of the country. The cry of Cŵn Anwn (or dogs of Anwn), for instance, is as familiar to the ears of the inhabitants of Ystradfellte and Pontneathvaughan [Pontneddfechan] as the watchman's rattle in . . . Covent-garden.

The area is certainly rich in legend and folklore. Cŵn Annwn, for example, referred to by Jones, were the hounds of the underworld. It was believed that their yelling or howling on dark nights foretold an imminent death in the locality. The dogs were supposed to watch for the souls of wicked men who were about to die. In general, however, they were harmless, and posed no threat to innocent people or their livestock.

The fairies, on the other hand, were notoriously fickle folk. One tale relates to Pen-fathor farm, two kilometres north of Ystradfellte. It was here that Morgan Rhys and his wife Modlen accidentally upset a fairy and set in motion a sequence of misfortunes: their cows were milked dry, crockery was broken in the kitchen, and an attempt was even made to steal a young baby from its mother's arms in the middle of the night. In desperation the family sought the advice of a wise old man, and it was he who eventually persuaded the fairies to leave the farm after he had tricked them into believing that Morgan and Modlen were living a life of extreme poverty.

But the best-known legend relates to a cave at Dinas Rock, near Pontneddfechan several miles down-valley of Porth yr Ogof. The tale begins far away in England:

A drover was once walking over London Bridge when a stranger engaged him in a very curious conversation. After a short while the stranger – a wizard – asked the drover where he had cut his walking stick, to which the Welshman replied:

'From a hazel thicket near my home.'

'Take me there, and I will show you treasure beyond your wildest dreams,' replied the wizard.

The Welshman was sceptical, but he had nothing to lose and together they headed for south Wales, and the Mellte valley. Then, after collecting some digging tools, they set off for Dinas Rock and the hazel thicket.

'Beneath the roots of this tree there lies a cave, and in this cave lies all manner of riches,' said the wizard.

The drover did as he was told and excavated a hole. Soon he located a large, flat slab. This was prised up to reveal a tunnel leading away into the darkness. Armed with a couple of candles, the pair entered the cave. As their eyes adjusted to the gloom, they found themselves on the threshold of a huge chamber. The cavern seemed to have a dim light of its own and in the gloom the drover could see scores of knights in armour, and a finely attired king, all fast asleep.

'King Arthur lies here awaiting the time when he will be summoned to save Wales from some great danger,' said the wizard.

At the far side of the chamber lay the treasure, but to reach it the drover had to tip-toe between the sleeping bodies and pass a large bell hanging from the ceiling.

'Take care not to touch the bell, or the knights will awake,' said the wizard. 'They will not take kindly to a false alarm or robbery.'

The drover took all the money that he could carry, concealed the cave entrance and headed home.

But all too soon the money was gone. On his return to the

cave the drover took more riches than before but, as he squeezed between the sleeping bodies, he brushed against the bell. The knights awoke and the drover was given a very severe beating. He stumbled home in a dreadful state.

From that time onward no trace has ever been found of the mysterious cave.

Cave life

Although not obvious to the inexperienced eye, life is to be found in caves. However, because there is no sunlight, no green plants grow deep underground. (Seeds which may be carried into the cave, on a boot, perhaps, or by water, will sometimes germinate but the plants will quickly wither and die.) Fungus is also occasionally found growing on rotting branches and tree trunks washed into the cave in time of flood.

Birds like the native dipper, or water blackbird as it is sometimes known, will frequently enter the daylight zone, the area within 10 or 15 metres of the entrance. Some may also find a suitable vantage point, build their nests and raise their young in the cave. Porth yr Ogof is also home to some bats (although it is not one of the best places to observe these creatures) in addition to frogs, flies and fish which occasionally and accidentally find their way into the cave by way of the river. Large numbers of bull-heads, for example, may be found in the Great Bedding Cave and these, like trout, seem to survive remarkably well, despite the fact that they are not adapted to the permanent darkness of the cave. Spiders, too, may be categorised as visitors or accidental cave dwellers.

Dipper

Genuine cave dwellers – creatures which live and re-produce underground, and known as **troglodytes** by cave scientists – are also found in Porth yr Ogof. However, not only will you not encounter the 'eel-like' proteus – a blind, white salamander found in caves on the continent and which may be up to 20 or 30 centimetres in length – it is extremely unlikely that you will notice any of the true cave dwellers also, because in Britain they are microscopic in size and appear as mere specks of white dust floating on the surface of small cave pools. Nevertheless, it is important to cultivate a respect for all the life forms which exist underground. Visitors should therefore try to make as little impact on the environment as humanly possible.

The exploration of Porth yr Ogof

Despite the fact that the cave has been visited by millions of people over the past century, we have no record of the first journey from the Main Entrance to the Resurgence. In all probability the 'dry' passages (all those containing air-spaces) would have been fairly thoroughly examined in the 1930s, when the first true pioneers of the sport visited the area from England.

In those early days Porth yr Ogof was very different to the cave we know today. Large sections of it were filled with quantities of driftwood, so much so that the area known today as the Maze was almost impassable. The ledges on either side of the Creek were liberally covered in deep piles of rotting twigs, decaying leaves and muddy sediment. Today, many scores of cavers explore these passages, with the result that virtually all of the fine silt and organic material has disappeared; the damp rock is completely bare and has been polished smooth by the passage of countless feet and slithering bodies.

The majority of those visiting Porth yr Ogof view the cave as a physical or mental challenge, or as a learning experience. Rarely does the question of real (original) exploration arise in the minds of most visitors for it is assumed that every nook and cranny has long since been thoroughly examined by someone at some time in the past.

To date (1998) the cave's passageways measure over 2.25 kilometres in length, and the surveyed network is depicted on page 12. Surprisingly, the system boasts 15 entrances but some of these are accessible only with the aid of specialist equipment. Cavers visiting Porth yr Ogof for the first time are usually shown the complex of passages adjoining the

The Letter Box squeeze is one of the most memorable parts of the underground visit

Main Entrance where it is possible to see a great variety of passage shapes and sizes. Easy walking passages lead gradually to more interesting terrain, where stooping gives way to crawling on hands and knees and, when confident, to challenging wriggles and squeezes. The best known squeeze is the Letter Box, located beneath one of the pothole entrances. This short section of bedding plane is 20 cm or less in height – less than the span of a fully outstretched adult hand! It is the sort of place that nurtures team spirit, where a helping hand is often much appreciated. Every team has its strengths and weaknesses and when confronted by an obstacle like the Letter Box, a caver quickly learns a lot about himself/herself and other members of his or her group.

Abseiling down into the cave on a rope is a very much more exciting means of entering the underground world than walking in via the Main Entrance. The Pothole Entrance is 10 metres deep and is normally only undertaken by older students. Indeed, vertical caving of this nature involves

The sump leading upstream from the Tradesman's Entrance is only accessible to fully equipped cave divers. Owing to the constrictions encountered along this passage, cave divers wear side-mounted air cylinders.

increased risks and the techniques of ropework demand the expertise of an experienced person. Novice cavers should never attempt such activity unless closely supervised. A second pothole, on the west side of the concrete pathway following the old, abandoned river bed between the Main Entrance and the Resurgence, allows cavers to climb down into the cave, but here again a lifeline, handled by an experienced leader, should always be used.

Many cavers leave the cave by following the river in a downstream direction from the Great Bedding Cave. At first the water is merely ankle deep but to reach the well-signposted 'safe exit' at the Shakehole Exit (a conspicuous plaque is attached to the wall), the group must negotiate a pool which is about waist deep. Depending upon the level of the river flowing through the cave, this route may be too wet, or too dangerous to attempt. Knowing when to alter course, when conditions may be uncertain or changing, only comes with experience. The force exerted by running water demands the

The large chamber lying between the Main Entrance and the Potholes

utmost respect. If the water flowing into the cave is knee deep at the Main Entrance, a cave leader would be ill-advised to attempt leaving the cave via the Shakehole Exit. Indeed, in such circumstances the experienced leader would use a rope as a handline at the Main Entrance in order to safeguard entry and exit along the west wall. If water levels are higher it is unwise to enter the cave.

The surveyed plan (see page 12) indicates that passages also extend away from the main centre of activity – the Main Entrance, the Creek and the Maze – to both east and north. These are completely flooded passages, or **sumps**, areas only accessible to experienced cave divers, with highly specialised equipment. Novice cavers should never be tempted to free dive even the shortest of sumps. A lungful of air may last a minute or so in a warm, relaxing swimming pool, but in a cold, claustrophobic cave passage it will last a mere fraction of that time. To get caught on some underwater projection, even momentarily, is critical and many highly experienced cavers have had worrying moments negotiating the shortest of watery obstacles.

Completely flooded passages should be avoided at all times, but even free-flowing streamways often present sections where the roof and water surface are close to one another. When an air-space is reduced to perhaps 30 cm or less the caver must negotiate the obstacle by ducking underwater. Under normal conditions, **ducks**, as they are called, provide a good sporting challenge and can be the source of a great deal of fun and amusement for everyone in the group. The Rat Trap, the pool at the head of the Creek, is such a place; cavers never forget the expressions on the faces (or indeed the language) of their friends who are required to negotiate this particular duck!

> But remember, water levels are constantly changing; all streamways, especially those in Porth yr Ogof, need to be treated with great caution.

Basic cave exploring equipment

The basic equipment consists of the following items:

Helmet: This must be robust and, ideally, should conform to the highest safety standards. It should fit snugly, and incorporate a 'Y' chin-strap and a suitable lamp bracket. Do not be tempted to wear a helmet designed for other purposes, i.e. a construction-workers helmet, without a chin-strap! One should never compromise on safety.

Lamp: Ideally this should be rechargeable and leakproof, although general-purpose, battery-powered head torches can be used, provided they are robust and can be securely attached to a helmet. Hand torches are not advisable, unless carried as a spare. Carbide lamps, which generate a naked flame illumination should be avoided. These can pose not only a safety hazard but also an environmental hazard.

Belt: Most caving lamps take their supply from a battery pack attached around the waist. It is important to use a belt appropriate to the type of battery being used. Given that a degree of vertical activity is possible, even in the simplest caves, it is worth purchasing a good, broad belt capable of being used for lifelining purposes.

Wellington boots: Rubber wellington boots are preferable to hill-walking boots. The wellington should possess a good deep tread, and be sufficiently large to allow for the wearing of two pairs of woollen socks. Footwear with minimal tread should not be used, nor boots with hooks which are used for lacing.

Clothing: It is assumed that anyone venturing into a cave for the first time will be supervised by an experienced and, preferably, qualified, caving instructor, and that novices will visit a site appropriate to their ability and aptitude. But whatever cave is visited, it must be stressed that the

Three young cavers examine the outflow from the Resurgence under normal water conditions.

temperature underground remains the same in summer and winter alike: caves are cold! In south Wales the temperature is about 7°C; caves in the north of Britain are colder. 'Wind chill' can make it feel colder still, as do wet clothes. One should always dress appropriately for the expected conditions. A fleece-type undersuit over a swimming costume, topped by a specialist one-piece oversuit is ideal but expensive. Old clothing will suffice at the outset but tight-fitting jeans should be avoided, as these can become very restrictive; a track-suit bottom is far better. Woollen garments are strongly recommended for the upper body: a sweat shirt and a pullover at the very minimum. A waterproof anorak and trousers may help to keep the body dry, but a one-piece suit is much better.

Rather than purchase expensive equipment straight away, it is possible to hire gear from a specialist caving outlet. In this way the advantages and disadvantages of various items may be assessed. At a later date you can then buy precisely what you want, such as a wet suit for those really wet trips. Of course, those attending a caving course will be provided with all the basic equipment, which will normally include a one-piece caving oversuit. It is strongly advisable to adopt this entry into the caving world; there is no substitute for sound advice at the outset. Later, the novice may wish to join a club, and apart from any other advantages which this will bring, it may facilitate a small discount on equipment prices in particular shops.

Accessory equipment: Knee and elbow pads are frequently used by cavers. But as the caver gains experience he or she will be confronted by a host of other equipment, such as karabiners, personal survival bags, haul sacks and spare lighting.

Cave diver at the Resurgence

Is the exploration of Porth yr Ogof complete?

All the easily accessible parts of the cave have been thoroughly explored. However, the site's geography and detailed study of the cave survey (see page 12) will quickly reveal that the picture is not yet complete by any means. The flooded passages – the sumps – which lead off to the east and north remain to be negotiated. The dangers of exploring underwater in caves are considerable and even highly experienced and well-qualified open-water divers should not venture into these areas unless trained by specialists.

However, the few cave divers who have ventured into this murky and confined underwater realm have made some interesting discoveries. The map indicates that there is a considerable complex of flooded passageways at Porth yr Ogof, and an equally extensive series of dry passages beyond. Exploration of these areas did not begin until the late 1960s and the most northerly passages (the Parker Series) were not discovered until the mid 1970s. Because this area is difficult to reach, exploration is still incomplete. We know that the water which appears at the Tradesman's Entrance enters the limestone one kilometre away, at Church Sink. To date, about one third of this flooded route, known to cave divers as the Lower Cave Series, has been explored. It is possible that at some stage in the future cave divers will be able to enter a cave in the vicinity of Church Sink and emerge some hours later at Porth yr Ogof. It is equally possible that a far more extensive series of dry passages will be found heading to the east of the existing cave, in the vicinity of the Parker Series.

Another extensive complex is thought to exist to the west of the Mellte valley. There is an intriguing spring at the foot of the slope within the bounds of the dry river bed and opposite the point where the path descends into the cave.

Water-tracing experiments suggest that this spring is the outlet of a cave system which may trend north-west, beneath the hillside. It is extremely interesting, therefore, to speculate upon an underground connection being established between the caves of the upper afon Nedd to the west and afon Hepste to the east!

Outer space may be the final frontier for the explorers of the future but there is much more to be learnt about the ground beneath our feet. To go where no man (or woman) has been before is still possible and caves such as Porth yr Ogof present that very challenge today.

There are many places where small streams disappear underground in the Ystradfellte area. This site is called Pwll y Felin swallow hole (SN 942121), which lies close to the road, mid-way between the Hepste and Mellte valleys.

So you'd like to know more

Caves are found in a number of other areas, apart from south Wales. There are caves in north-east Wales and in Devon, the Mendip Hills, the Forest of Dean, the Peak District of Derbyshire, the Furness area of Cumbria, and the Yorkshire Dales where the systems are very extensive. Further north, there are caves in Scotland and many are also to be found the length and breadth of Ireland. The caves in all these areas are described in guide books obtainable in specialist caving shops. Local libraries may also keep some caving literature on their shelves, and they are usually happy to order other works on request. A broader range of current caving literature can be purchased at outdoor shops, books which will convince many readers that caving presents not only an exciting physical pursuit but also an opportunity to see some of most beautiful wilderness areas on earth.

Those who wish to pursue the sport beyond the introductory level of Porth yr Ogof have several options. A degree of training and guidance is essential, so ask an instructor for his or her views; many outdoor-pursuit centres and professional instructors run a range of caving courses to suit varying needs. Specialist caver-training videos have been produced and these are recommended viewing for all newcomers to the sport. Bad habits are all too easily acquired: all cavers are therefore urged to do things in a responsible manner and help maintain the underground environment for the enjoyment of all.

A FEW SAFETY RULES

Should you decide to organise your own cave visit, it is important to remember the following points:

1. Unless you are already very experienced, **never go into a cave alone**. A group of four is recommended. Should a member of the group be unfortunate enough to have an accident, one person can remain in the cave to comfort and support the casualty, while the other two make their way out to alert the Cave Rescue Organisation.

2. **Read the cave guide** and, when planning your trip, take advice from those who are familiar with the site.

3. Always **take note of the weather forecast**: caves such as Porth yr Ogof are prone to flooding, whilst others may entail a long walk to reach the entrance.

4. **Always tell a responsible person where you are going (preferably in writing to avoid confusion) and your expected time of return.** If you fail to return, for whatever reason, help can then be sent to the scene. It is important that you adhere to your times in order to avoid unnecessary worry and, possibly, wasting other people's time and money.

5. **Always carry a spare, reliable light** for emergency use, and a small first aid/survival pack.

6. Always carry some **emergency food**, such as chocolate bars.

7. Do bear in mind that the land on which a cave entrance is situated is owned by someone else. **Always refer to a cave guide for the recommended access procedures.** To upset a landowner or local resident is to risk the loss of access for other cavers in the future.

8. **Caves are vulnerable** and should be treated with respect. Damage, accidental or otherwise, is irreparable. Please do not dispose of any rubbish, such as sweet wrappers, in the cave or despoil the site in any way. Conservation is of the utmost importance; try and leave the cave in a better state than you found it.

WARNING

While much of Porth yr Ogof is as 'safe' as any accessible cave, the deep water areas have claimed the lives of at least ten people since 1957 (see Appendix 1). Most of those who died were novice cavers being guided through the system. Although the pools may appear challenging and easy to cross, the water is exceptionally cold, even at the height of summer, and sudden immersion can result in extreme shock which may, in turn, trigger a tragic accident.

Leaders of inexperienced parties, therefore, should not venture into deep-water areas. Experienced cavers should ensure that the following conditions are satisfied before entering deep water:

1) that each person is equipped with a wet suit and buoyancy aid;
2) that each person is a confident swimmer;
3) that a suitably prepared life-saver is on hand.

All leaders should be fully aware of their moral and legal responsibilities, and be familiar with the location of the nearest phone. When the car park at Porth yr Ogof is manned there is a phone (for emergency use only) in the attendant's hut; at other times there is an emergency phone near the rear of the hut. It is important to bear in mind that mobile phone reception may **NOT** be available on the valley floor!

In the event of an accident in the cave, the number to contact is 999 – Cave Rescue

23 June 1957	Leonard Garaway (aged 20 years): experienced caver
20 June 1966	B. Speakman (age not known): experience not known
7 August 1968	Anthony Stannard (aged 28 years): experienced caver
18 October 1970	Stephen Sedgewick (aged 18 years): novice caver
13 February 1971	Paul Esser (aged 21 years): trainee cave diver*
19 July 1973	Graham Alston (aged 15 years): cadet soldier; novice caver
22 July 1981	Adrian Luck (aged 28 years): novice caver
28 July 1986	Gwynfor Hughes (aged 45 years): instructor (leading a party)
16 June 1992	Amanda Stead (aged 26 years): army cadet; novice caver
14 October 1992	Graham Lipp (aged 34 years): cave instructor (leading a party)

With the exeption of the Esser incident, all the fatalities occurred within sight of daylight, in the Resurgence pool at the downstream terminus of the cave. There have also been a great many 'near misses' within the cave, at the Resurgence pool, the White Horse Pool and upstream of the Tradesman's Entrance.

* Esser was attempting a solo dive from the Tradesman's Entrance to the Top Entrance, a distance of over 200 metres. For reasons not fully understood he followed the wrong line and ran out of air.

Under flood conditions the Resurgence is filled to the roof and water emerges under considerable pressure, exhibiting something of a 'mushroom' effect.

Many people would argue that fatalities at Porth yr Ogof are avoidable. Without question, there is need for great vigilance, particularly where novices are involved and where cavers are in contact with deep, cold water. However, considering the large number of warning notices both outside and inside the cave, coupled with the fact that two of the last three fatalities involved experienced cavers in charge of parties of young people, some individuals have suggested that the accidents at Porth yr Ogof have been triggered by supernatural forces. It has been claimed that ley lines, lines of earth energy, may account for a particular 'atmosphere' at certain places. Such lines may be positive or negative, the latter sometimes referred to as 'black streams'. One researcher in this field has suggested that there is a concentration of negative streams at the Resurgence pool of Porth yr Ogof, where the cave water re-emerges at the surface. 'Entities' – ghosts or malevolent spirits – are said to be associated with such negative streams which, it is claimed, also exist at points other than at the Resurgence. But there are no references to such 'spirits' or 'ghosts' in local folklore.

Appendix 2: Cave facts

The longest cave in Wales is Ogof Ddraenen near Blaenafon, which boasts over 63 km of explored passage.

The longest cave in Britain is the Lancaster-Easegill complex, near Ingleton, in the Yorkshire Dales National Park. This has over 70 km of explored passage.

The longest cave in the world is Mammoth Cave, Kentucky, USA, with over 563 km of passage.

The largest cave chamber in the world is Sarawak Chamber in the Gunong Mulu National Park, Malaysia. It is 700 metres long, some 300 metres wide and at least 70 metres high.

The world's deepest cave is the Gouffre Mirolda, near Samoens in the French Alps. It is 1,610 metres deep.

The deepest shaft in the world is El Sotano, in northern Mexico. This has a 'free-fall' drop of 410 metres (1,346 feet) from top to bottom.

The deepest underground pitch in the world is 410 metres, in Abatz Cave in Georgia, formerly part of the USSR.

Caves are not found solely in limestone. Small caves are etched by the action of wind and waves. Tunnels are also common beneath glaciers. However, the longest caves formed in rock other than limestone are lava tubes, formed by the flow of molten lava away from an erupting volcano. The world's longest lava tube is Kazamura Cave, 61 km in length, and found on the island of Hawaii.

Further Reading

Martyn Farr, *The Darkness Beckons*, Diadem, ISBN 0 906371 87 2.

Martyn Farr, *Darkworld—The Secrets of Llangattock Mountain*, Gomer Press, ISBN 1 85902 501 3.

Trevor Ford, *Limestones & Caves of Wales*, Cambridge University Press, ISBN 0 521 32438 6.

Chris Howes, *Images Below*, Wild Places, Cardiff, ISBN 0 9526701 1 9.

David Judson, *Caving Practice and Equipment*, David & Charles, ISBN 0 7153 8155 5.

Mike Simms, *Caves and Karst of the Brecon Beacons National Park*, British Cave Research Association, ISBN 0 900265 20 5.

Tim Stratford, *Caves of South Wales*, Cordee, ISBN 1 871890 03 9.

Descent—a magazine published bi-monthly by Gloster Publications Ltd.

Acknowledgements

The author gratefully acknowledges the following people and organisations for their help with the production of this booklet. The map showing the layout of the entire cave system was based upon an original survey undertaken by the University of Bristol Spaeleological Society and the Cave Diving Group of Great Britain. The Brecon Beacons National Park Authority kindly supplied information regarding land ownership and site management.

I am particularly indebted to my friends Pat Cronin, Peter Fowler and others for their patient assistance with photography. For the use of the historical engraving of the cave, I am obliged to Chris Howes. Sincere appreciation is also extended to Pat Cronin and Peter Fowler for their comments on the text, and I am deeply beholden to Peter for redrawing my rudimentary maps and diagrams. Thank you all.

Clun Gwyn waterfall a kilometre downstream of Porth yr Ogof, is one of a series of spectacular falls along the course of afon Mellte.

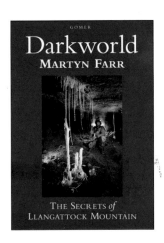

'*Darkworld* is handsomely illustrated with well-reproduced pictures, mostly in colour, representing the best underground scenery.'

Descent

'I have to say that this book is a real gem and one which will give you many hours of enjoyable reading. Even if you have never visited the South Wales karst you will enjoy this book and find it difficult to put down . . . Don't miss out, buy this one.'

The International Caver

£15.95 Hardback ISBN 1 85902 501 3
£12.95 Softback ISBN 1 85902 595 1

First Impression—1998

ISBN 1 85902 559 5

© Martyn Farr

Martyn Farr has asserted his right under the Copyright, Designs and Patents Act, 1988, to be identified as Author of this Work.

Printed at Gomer Press, Llandysul, Ceredigion, Wales